INTRODUCTION

Have you been to a gallery before? If not then you will have a very interesting day. You may go to see the 'star attraction' or a special exhibition, but there will be many other things to see, so make the most of your i-SPY book to guide you around. Paintings or sculpture; modern or Renaissance; landscapes or portraits; land or sea; minimalist or pop art: there is something for everyone. Some galleries specialize in photography or sculpture and a few artists in particular, but most will give you the opportunity to see lots of different styles from several centuries by many artists so you can look around and decide what you find the most interesting. There may be a gallery trail that you can follow, ask at the information desk.

Perhaps you will find a landscape of a place you have visited, or it might be an exotic location. Maybe you will see a delicate botanical painting of a plant you recognize. Alternatively there might be sculptures of sports or dance, or something very original and different. Art is to be enjoyed, but it can make you think too. Can you work out what is happening in a picture? Did the artist include anything in the painting for you to find? Is a painting just not what it appears to be at all! Galleries put information cards next to each piece of work so if something catches your eye you can find out more about it. If your visit has inspired you, look out for areas where you can create your own art or try something when you get back home.

How to use your i-SPY book

As you work through this book, you will notice that the subjects are arranged in groups loosely based on the kind of art they represent. You need 1000 points to send off for your i-SPY certificate (see page 64) but that is not too difficult because there are masses of points in every book. Each entry has a star or circle and points value beside it. The stars represent harder to spot entries. As you make each i-SPY, write your score in the circle or star.

Points: 15

PURPOSE-BUILT GALLERY

Many art galleries are in a purpose-built building whose architecture is often a work of art in itself. This is the National Gallery in London, which was built to house the national collection of art and opened in 1838.

CONVERTED BUILDING

Points: 25

DavidGrahamB6 / Shutterstock.com

Many of the newer galleries around the country have been created in converted older buildings. Several of these used to be old factories! This is the BALTIC Centre in Gateshead, which used to be a flour mill. Score if your gallery is in a converted building of any kind.

INFORMATION DESK

Points: 5

You will probably start your visit at the information or entrance desk, where you will usually be told about special events and tours.

Points: 5

DONATION BOX

Some galleries charge a fee to enter but others are free. The free ones will often have a donation box that allows people to donate if they want to contribute to the gallery's running costs.

SECURITY GUARD

Points: 5

Galleries usually contain many valuable items, so there are often security guards about.

Blend Images / Alamy Stock Photo

Points: 10

The entrance area will typically have a map or plan of the gallery on the wall, or you may have been given a plan at the entrance or information desk.

PUBLIC DISPLAY

Points: 10

Galleries these days like to interact with their local communities. Many will have exhibitions near the entrance where visitors or local schools have their art on display.

Lapina / Shutterstock.com

SOMEONE TAKING A PHOTOGRAPH

Points: 10

Many galleries do not allow you to take photographs of the artworks, but some galleries do, and sometimes you'll see people taking a sneaky photo anyway.

Points: 5 ## SOMEONE STUDYING A PICTURE

Art can be complicated and sometimes it takes a lot of studying to appreciate everything the artist wanted to show.

SOMEONE USING AN AUDIO GUIDE   Points: 10

Many galleries offer audio guides to visitors. They tell you about the different exhibits as you go around.

Points: 10   SOMEONE SKETCHING

Seeing so many works of art in one place makes some people want to have a go themselves, or possibly just try to record the art for future reference.

PAINTINGS

The most common type of art you will find in the average gallery is paintings. There are paintings of places, people, animals, objects, events and almost anything you can imagine.

LANDSCAPE PAINTING WITH A CHURCH

 Points: 15

Paintings of places are often called landscape paintings. Sometimes they will be of countryside with one or two buildings in them. Score 15 points for any landscape painting containing a church.

LANDSCAPE PAINTING WITH FARM ANIMALS

Farm scenes have been popular subjects over the years. Score 10 points for a landscape with some farm animals in it.

Points: 10

LANDSCAPE PAINTING WITH A RAINBOW

The weather is always a popular subject in Britain. Score 15 points for a landscape with a rainbow.

Points: 15

FAMOUS LANDSCAPE PAINTING

Originally, landscapes were only painted as the background to a portrait. In the eighteenth century artists such as Thomas Gainsborough, John Constable and J. M. W. Turner became famous for making the landscape itself into the subject.

Constable was inspired by the countryside around his childhood home and depicted a romantic, peaceful side of rural England in many of his paintings, such as this one of Flatford Mill. Score for spotting any of Constable's landscape paintings.

Top Spot! **Points: 50** 50

Points: 15

SEASCAPE

Paintings of scenes on the sea or oceans are often referred to as seascapes. With vivid colours for the sea and the sky and images of crashing waves and swirling waters, they can look particularly dramatic.

FAMOUS SEASCAPE PAINTING

Painting at a similar time to Constable (see page 9), Joseph Turner was famed for his evocative seascapes that typically show richly coloured raging seas and turbulent tides. This one is entitled *The Slave Ship* and is typical of Turner's work with the deep, rich layers in the sky and sea almost merging together. Score for spotting any Turner seascape.

Top Spot! **Points: 50**

Points: 10

CITYSCAPE

The hustle and bustle of towns and cities has been the inspiration for many artists over the years.

BATTLE SCENE

Points: 10

Battles have been the scene of many decisive moments in history and have often been immortalised in paintings. This one is of the Charge of the Light Brigade, but you can score for any battle scene.

Paintings that show a person or a group of people in close-up are called portrait paintings.

Points: 5

PORTRAIT PAINTING OF A WOMAN

Many portrait paintings are of the head and shoulders, but they can include the whole person or more than one person.

PORTRAIT PAINTING OF A MAN

Important or wealthy men were often the subjects of early portraits. Before cameras were invented, it was the only way that someone could have a picture of themselves.

Points: 5

PORTRAIT PAINTING OF A CHILD

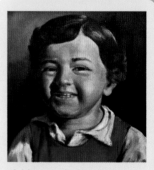

Children are less common subjects of historical portraits.

Points: 5

12

Points: 20

ROYAL PORTRAIT

As mentioned, early portraits were often of important or wealthy men, and the wealthiest and most important were the European Kings. Henry VIII was painted many times. This is a famous portrait of his that was painted by Hans Holbein. Score for a portrait of any royal person.

SELF-PORTRAIT

Points: 20

A very popular choice of subject for many artists over the years has been the artist themselves. This is a famous self-portrait by Vincent Van Gogh who painted himself at least thirty times during his lifetime. Score for any self-portrait.

The popularity of subject matter for paintings is always changing, but certain compositions have remained popular throughout the years.

STILL LIFE WITH FRUIT

Points: 5

A 'still life' is a composition that shows a collection of everyday objects. Fruit, plants, bowls and glassware are common elements in still lifes.

Points: 20

STILL LIFE WITH A MUSICAL INSTRUMENT

Occasionally there will be a musical instrument in the composition.

Points: 10

FLOWERS

Their varied colours and textures have made flowers popular subjects for artists since the early days of art.

ANIMAL

Points: 10

Animals are commonly seen in paintings, whether they are in the wild, working animals or pets.

Points: 15

SEASONS

The change in season allows the artist to paint the same scene with a totally different appearance. Autumn colours are always very popular!

Before the turn of the 19th century a lot of artists were inspired by their religious beliefs. As such a large number of older paintings in galleries around the country depict religious scenes.

PAINTING OF CHRIST AS A CHILD   Points: 10

Due to the predominance of Christianity throughout Europe in the last millennium many paintings in galleries show images of Christ. Score 10 points for an image of Christ as a child.

PAINTING OF CHRIST AS AN ADULT

Images of Christ as an adult should be easily found in most galleries.

Points: 10

PAINTING OF MARY

Images of the Virgin Mary are less common but still quite easy to find.

Points: 10

Points: 10

HINDU PAINTING

Many galleries around the country will have paintings representing other religions. Here is a Hindu painting of Vishnu. Score 10 points for any painting representing one of the other traditional religions such as Hinduism, Judaism, Islam or Buddhism.

Claudine Van Massenhove / Shutterstock.com

BUDDHIST PAINTING

Points: 10

Here is another example of a religious painting, this time depicting the Buddha, whose teachings form the foundations of Buddhism. Score another 10 points if you can find a second picture depicting a different religion.

Jokei / Shutterstock.com

The period between the 14th and 16th centuries is known as the Renaissance. This was a particularly productive time for artists especially in Italy and then later across most of Europe.

Points: 25

DA VINCI

Some of the most famous artists of this time were Leonardo Da Vinci, Michelangelo and Raphael. Score 25 points for spotting a painting by any one of these three. This picture is of The Last Supper, by Da Vinci.

BOTTICELLI

Points: 25

Botticelli is associated with the early part of the Renaissance period. At the height of his fame he was regarded as one of the best artists in Italy.

Points: 25

TITIAN

Titian was another Italian Renaissance painter, whose art has always been popular. Score 25 points for one of his paintings.

Points: 30

EL GRECO

As the Renaissance influence spread across Europe, paintings in that style started being produced in Spain, France, Germany and the Low Countries. Originally from Crete, El Greco was a Renaissance artist who did much of his best work while living in Spain.

GERMAN AND DUTCH RENAISSANCE ART

Points: 30

Dutch and German painters first copied and then adapted the Renaissance style in their painting at this time. Find a German or Dutch painting painted between 1490 and 1550 to score 30 points.

From around 1600 to 1750 European art was dominated by the Baroque movement. Famous painters like Caravaggio, Rubens, Rembrandt and Vermeer tried to capture dramatic moments in time, and emphasized the contrast between darkness and light.

Points: 50   **Top Spot!**

USE OF LIGHT

Many baroque paintings try to show the real effect of a light source on a composition, like this one by Johannes Vermeer. Find a baroque painting that has distinct areas of darkness and light.

DRAMATIC MOMENT

Points: 25

Lots of baroque paintings depict a moment of extreme tension or drama. Spot a dramatic baroque painting for 25 points.

Points: 25

BAROQUE PORTRAIT

Professional portrait painting became more popular during this period and many famous portraits were produced. This one is *The Laughing Cavalier* by Frans Hals. Spot a portrait painted between 1600 and 1750 for 25 points.

Towards the end of the 19th century artists started to deviate from the traditional style of painting that had been around for hundreds of years. This became known as 'modern art'. The Modern Art movement has produced a huge range of artworks from a variety of different styles.

Impressionism is considered by some to be the first kind of modern art. Impressionist paintings concentrate on capturing the feel and emotion of a scene rather than producing a faithful reproduction of it. They will usually have visible brush strokes and an almost hurried, unfinished look.

IMPRESSIONIST LANDSCAPE

Points: 10

The shapes do not need to be painted in a realistic way to create the desired atmosphere in an impressionist painting.

FAMOUS IMPRESSIONIST LANDSCAPE

The most famous impressionist painters were all working in the late 1800s and early 1900s. This example is by Monet, but score points for a landscape painting by him, Degas, Pissarro, Renoir or Sisley.

 Points: 30

Points: 15

IMPRESSIONIST PORTRAIT

Portraits in the impressionist style are often slightly more realistic looking than landscapes, though you can still see the brush strokes if you look hard enough.

FAMOUS IMPRESSIONIST PORTRAIT

Some of the most famous impressionist painters concentrated on landscapes while others concentrated on portraits. This painting is by Degas who painted both, so score for a portrait by him or by Cassatt, Caillebotte, or Manet.

Points: 30

23

At the turn of the 20th century artists began trying to endow their paintings with more of their own emotions. Rather than just capturing the world in an observational way, they started adding more meaning to their works. The styles used varied greatly but can be grouped together under the term 'post-impressionism'.

Points: 25

POST-IMPRESSIONIST LANDSCAPE

Van Gogh is one of the most famous painters of the time. He painted still lifes, landscapes and portraits. Score 25 points for any Van Gogh landscape.

POST-IMPRESSIONIST PORTRAIT

Points: 15

Other famous post-impressionists were Gauguin, Seurat and Paul Cézanne. Cézanne's early works were in the impressionist style but he moved away from this style in later life. Score 15 points for a portrait by any post-impressionist artist.

As painters added more and more of their own meaning into their work, this grew into the Expressionist movement. Subjects became more difficult to decipher and in some examples it can be hard to work out any specific, recognisable elements at all amongst a collection of shapes and colours.

Points: 20

EXPRESSIONISM

This painting, called *Composition VII*, was painted by the Russian artist Wassily Kandinsky in 1913. He painted it in Germany, the birthplace of expressionism, and used colourful, abstract forms to explore musical concepts in the form of painting. Like all expressionist paintings the aim is to stir the emotions of the viewer. Other famous expressionists were Ernst Ludwig Kirchner, Oskar Kokoschka and Edvard Munch. Score 20 points for any expressionist painting you find.

COLOURED LANDSCAPE

Points: 25

As expression and emotion became more important to painters, more abstract colours and shapes were introduced. Find a landscape painting with an artificially coloured landscape.

LANDSCAPE WITH A HIDDEN SUBJECT

The style of the painting can often be used to hide the subject from a casual look. Study a modern landscape to find a hidden building. You can practise by trying to spot the cathedral in this painting by Pierre Dumont.

Points: 50 **Top Spot!**

Points: 10

MODERN PORTRAIT

As photography developed, artists were no longer relied upon to capture realistic portraits of their subjects. This freed them to experiment with different ways of representing people and using bright colours and abstract backgrounds to help portray something of their characters. Score for any modern portrait that uses bright colours.

CUBIST PORTRAIT

Points: 20

Some modern portraits also use shapes. This is an example of cubism, a type of modern art where the subject is made up of many geometric shapes.

Points: 30

CUBIST STILL LIFE

There are even cubist still lifes. These are much more abstract than the traditional still life, because the artist effectively breaks up the objects and shows them from several different viewpoints within the same painting.

UNUSUAL SUBJECT

Points: 20

There are movements within modern art that deal with strange and unusual compositions, or futuristic paintings. Find an unusual or unrealistic composition for 20 points.

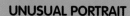

Points: 15

UNUSUAL PORTRAIT

Modern art portraits can make you think. Find a distorted portrait or one that has a strange aspect to it, like the hands on this one.

28

MINIMALISM

Points: 20

Some types of paintings fall into a category called Minimalist. They usually only include a few shapes or sometimes even just one! Find any painting made up of less than 3 shapes.

Points: 20

PATTERNS

Other modern art images look like a collection of random squiggles and splashes. Score for any squiggly pattern!

Paintings are being produced all of the time. All new and recently finished paintings are referred to as 'contemporary art', but they may be in any style from history or a new style altogether.

CONTEMPORARY LANDSCAPE

Points: 5

Find a landscape painting that has been painted in the last five years for 5 points.

Points: 5

CONTEMPORARY PORTRAIT

Find a painting of a person or group of people that has been painted in the last five years for 5 points.

CONTEMPORARY OBJECTS

Points: 10

Score 10 points if you find a recently painted still life.

Points: 15

CONTEMPORARY PLACES

Busy city street scenes are popular subjects for contemporary artists. Find a contemporary painting of a recognisable town or city for 15 points.

Many galleries will have drawings or sketches on display. They can be the working sketches that famous painters used to plan out their paintings, or finished works in their own right.

LANDSCAPE SKETCH

Points: 15

The lines in a sketch can often capture as much detail as a painting.

 Points: 15

PORTRAIT SKETCH

In many cities around the world sketch artists will draw a quick portrait of you for a small fee. Some of these sketches end up in galleries.

WORKING SKETCH

Top Spot! Points: 50 50

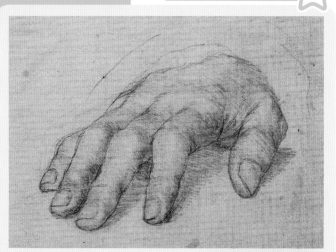

Some painters sketch their composition first for practice. Here is a sketch of a hand from a famous painting and below it is the final painting. Score 50 points if you can spot a sketch that was used as practice for a piece of art, or for elements within it.

Points: 25

SKETCH BY FAMOUS PAINTER

Many artists have dabbled in more than one art form, perhaps working in drawing, painting and sculpture. Here is one of Botticelli's sketches for an illustration in Dante's *Divine Comedy*. Score 25 points if you can find a sketch by an artist who is also a famous painter or sculptor.

PEN AND INK DRAWING

Points: 15

Ink can give a very precise finish, especially to subjects with hard lines like buildings.

PASTEL DRAWING

Points: 20

Pastels offer a softer finish than paint, but still allow for a variety of colours, shapes and effects.

Points: 20

ENGRAVING

Engraving involves scratching a series of lines or dots onto metal or glass to make up a picture. This technique takes a long time to master.

ETCHING

Points: 20

Etching is similar to engraving but uses acid to burn the image onto the surface.

50 Points: 50   Top Spot!

GRAFFITI ART

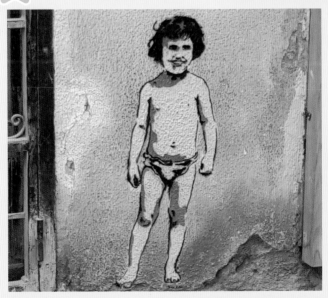

Graffiti is typically drawn or painted onto the outside walls of buildings. It can take the form of stylized words or 'tags' (the name given to an individual artist's distinctive signature), fantasy pictures or real life compositions. Historically graffiti was unwanted and often considered as being criminal damage, but in more recent years some have become recognised as works of art and the most famous graffiti artists can find their work is highly sought after. Due to its nature you will do well to find it in a gallery, but there are occasional exhibitions. Score if you see any graffiti art at the gallery or on the street.

Pop Art is a style of art that uses mundane and commonplace objects from everyday life and turns them into art. It takes its influences from movies, cartoons, pop music, advertisements and even packaging, and may be painted, drawn or printed.

POP ART IN CARTOON STYLE

Points: 15

Artists such as Roy Lichtenstein made bold, cartoon-style pop art popular in the 1960s.

POP ART WITH EVERYDAY OBJECT

Points: 25

Some of the famous pop art images use one everyday object repeated over and over, or repeated with a different colour scheme applied.

Statues and other sculptures can often be seen dotted about inside galleries and sometimes also outside the entrance or in the grounds.

BRONZE

Points: 5

Metal sculptures are made by a process called casting, which involves pouring molten metal into a mould and leaving it to harden as it cools. Bronze has been a popular metal used in casting for thousands of years.

Anna Pakutina / Shutterstock.com

Points: 5

MARBLE

The translucent and relatively soft qualities of this stone make it a popular choice for sculptors wishing to create statues with a smooth, polished finish. They use different tools such as mallets, chisels and rasps to carve the stone into the required shape.

PERSON

Points: 10

People have always been popular subjects for the sculptor, whether they are from mythology or real life.

Points: 25

ANIMAL

Animal sculptures are a lot more rare, so finding one of these could be tricky.

Busts are statues that show the head and neck of a person, and sometimes also the shoulders.

BRONZE BUST

Points: 15

Busts have been made for hundreds of years. They are typically of Kings, Queens and other important people.

 Points: 25

ALABASTER BUST

Alabaster is similar in appearance to marble, but lighter and softer. It is also more translucent than marble.

TERRACOTTA BUST

Points: 20

Terracotta is clay-based, making it easier to work with than stone or metal. The chance to remodel and rework the material can lead to very detailed sculptures.

15 · **Points: 15**

MODERN SCULPTURE

Modern sculptures may be made of almost any type of material and are not necessarily 'sculpted' in the traditional sense, but instead may have been constructed.

Adriano Castelli / Shutterstock.com

SPOOKY SCULPTURE

Points: 25

Sinister, unusual and thought-provoking shapes are quite common.

fritzié / Shutterstock.com

Points: 5

5

INDOOR SCULPTURE

Some sculptures are definitely made to be housed within a building, like this one of a lady reclining in a bed.

OUTDOOR SCULPTURE

Points: 15

15

Other sculptures are designed to be displayed outside. They may be very large and have reflective surfaces so the changing daylight can affect the appearance of the sculpture.

Points: 25

ON THE WAY TO THE GALLERY

Phillip Maguire / Shutterstock.com

If you keep an eye out you will see that there is a lot of public art on display around the country. You might even see some on the way to the gallery. It might be made of metal, stone or wood, or a man-made material like fibreglass or perspex, and may also involve water. Award yourself 25 points for any that you see.

Galleries will often contain artistic objects that are neither paintings, statues or sculptures. See if you can find some of these items in your gallery.

FURNITURE

Points: 10

Many galleries feature antique or unusual pieces of furniture. Chairs are particularly popular.

Points: 15

CLOCK

Clocks, while being useful, can also be works of art in their own right.

Premier Photo / Shutterstock.com

Smaller artistic items that are not paintings, statues or furniture can be grouped under the description of 'objet d'art', which in French literally means object of art. These can include jewellery, belt buckles, vases, ornate boxes, glassware and many other things.

VASE OR URN

Points: 10

Made from a variety of different materials, some of them dating from a long time ago, decorative vases and urns can be seen in many galleries.

 Points: 15

PORCELAIN

This type of ceramic is used to make some very fine pieces, including tea sets, vases and plates.

JEWELLERY

Points: 15

Items of jewellery, especially those useful things like buckles and brooches, can be seen in some galleries.

INSTALLATION ART

In the larger galleries around the country there are whole rooms and spaces given over to artists to create installations.

Points: 20

ROOF INSTALLATION

An unusual perspective can be achieved by suspending art from the roof or ceiling.

3D PAINTING

Points: 15

Like a painting but protruding from the wall (either actually or perceptively), a 3D painting can draw the visitor inside in a way that a 2D painting may not be able to do.

 Points: 15

LIGHTS

An installation made up of lights, static or changing, can be an exciting find.

SHAPES, PATTERNS OR COLOURS

Points: 20

Occasionally the whole space is filled up with many different items, allowing the artist to experiment with shapes, colours and textures. Score for any installation with more than 5 separate objects.

 Points: 25

EVERYDAY OBJECTS

Arranging a number of everyday objects together to create a different shape can make you see them in a very different way!

INSTALLATION ART

OUTDOOR INSTALLATION

Points: 10

Some installations need to be outside, such as this sculptured landform in the grounds of the Scottish National Gallery of Modern Art in Edinburgh.

Points: 20

WALK-THROUGH INSTALLATION

Other installations let you walk through them and experience them from different angles.

Ron Ellis / Shutterstock.com

INTERACTIVE INSTALLATION

artition / Shutterstock.com

Galleries of modern art are increasingly playing host to interactive art installations, where the viewers are invited to get involved with the art and become a part of it. This type of art varies greatly, from virtual Internet art and electronic art, to the example shown in the photograph: a simple cage with soft matting where people can relax and play. Score for any art installation that you can interact with.

Top Spot!   Points: 40

49

PHOTOGRAPHS

The first grainy black and white photographs were taken in the middle of the 19th century and within 50 years photography was becoming a popular way of capturing views and memories. Galleries will often have exhibitions of famous photographers' work or photographs of important events.

Points: 20

OLD LANDSCAPE PHOTOGRAPH

Landscapes made better subjects than people for early photographs because they did not move during the long exposure time required. Score for any 19th century landscape.

MODERN LANDSCAPE PHOTOGRAPH

Points: 5

Modern landscape photography can include dramatic vistas and massive panoramas. Score for any modern landscape photograph.

 Points: 5

CITYSCAPE PHOTOGRAPH

The ever-changing urban landscape is always a popular subject for photographers, and can look very dramatic when it is lit up at night.

OLD PORTRAIT PHOTOGRAPH

Points: 20

Families, businesses and teams would often get group photographs taken. The people would have to remain very still for several minutes to allow for the long exposure times of the camera, which is one reason why they always looked so serious! Score for a 19th century photo of a group of people.

Points: 10

ROYAL PHOTOGRAPH

Public interest in the Royal Family has always made them popular subjects for photographers, whether they are attending state events or at more informal occasions.

PHOTOJOURNALISM

Points: 25

Exhibitions of famous press photographers' work can be interesting and enlightening. They often capture important moments in time, illustrating stories that are in the news and which affect our world.

Points: 40   **Top Spot!**

WAR PHOTOGRAPH

War photographs taken by people at the front with the troops can also be very powerful and give an insight into a world that most of us never see.

SPORTS PHOTOGRAPH

Points: 15

Marcos / Mesa Sam Wordley / Shutterstock.com

The best photographers can capture the skill and excitement on display during a sporting event. Their photographs can make for colourful exhibitions.

Points: 15

PAPARAZZI PHOTOGRAPH

Paparazzi is the name given to photographers who follow celebrities around, trying to get the next scoop. The best have had their own exhibitions in galleries in recent years.

AERIAL PHOTOGRAPH

Points: 10

Photographs taken from the sky can provide jaw-dropping imagery of the planet. Aerial photographs were traditionally taken from aeroplanes or helicopters, but increasingly drones are now being used.

Points: 5

NATURE PHOTOGRAPH

It can take a lot of patience waiting around for the perfect moment to capture nature in action, but it can lead to stunning results.

ZOOM/MACRO PHOTOGRAPH

Points: 15

This type of photography captures objects in the minutest detail. It is very effective for flowers and insects. Score points for any close-up image.

 Points: 20

UNDERWATER PHOTOGRAPH

Special underwater cameras allow the world beneath the waves to be explored and viewed by people on dry land.

ASTROPHOTOGRAPH

Points: 15

The night sky and the universe beyond can be the subjects of stunning photography. This image is known as a 'star trail' and is taken by attaching a camera to a tripod and leaving the shutter open for a long period of time. The movement of individual stars across the night sky is shown in the series of curved lines. Other astrophotographs may be of individual stars, nebulae, planets or galaxies taken with powerful telephoto lenses.

Points: 25

In its simplest form, animation involves taking a series of photographs of a drawn subject; in each drawing the subject is in a slightly different position so that when the photographs are viewed in sequence as a film, the subject appears to be moving. Puppets or clay models may also be used instead of drawings.

An animation on display in a gallery is likely to be a more sophisticated composition than the simple form shown here, perhaps illustrating an unusual idea. You may find either individual shots (called 'stills') or a complete film on display; score points for either.

ART FILM

Points: 25

Many artists have made films to get their ideas across. These may be very short, or very long, or even on an endless loop! The films you see in a gallery will usually make you think or challenge your normal views.

 Points: 50   **Top Spot!**

VIRTUAL REALITY

Virtual reality is becoming more common in galleries as a way of letting the visitor experience art. Most VR uses headsets over the eyes and ears so you feel like you are in the artwork.

DRAW SOMETHING

Points: 25

In many galleries there are places where you can have a go at creating art yourself. If not you can draw something while you are going around the gallery.

Points: 25

PAINT SOMETHING

You won't be able to paint something while you are wandering around but you might be lucky enough to be in a gallery that has a painting area.

SCULPT SOMETHING

Points: 25

Some galleries will let you have a go at making something with your hands, but you might have to go back to collect it at a later date when it is dry!

Points: 10

STAY BACK

Wherever you go and whatever you do in the gallery, never cross these roped barriers! Score 10 points if you see one though.

WAITER OR BARISTA

Points: 5

If you go to the café for a bite to eat look out for the serving staff for some easy points.

Points: 10

SWEET TREAT

mmmmm...

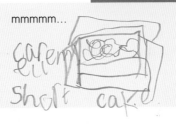

SOMEONE HAVING A RELAXING DRINK

Points: 5

Top up your points by spotting some people chatting and having a break.

Points: 5

5

Most galleries have a gift shop where you can stock up on your art books and posters.

PAINTS SET

Points: 10

10

You might need one of these if you want to recreate all the art you've seen on your visit.

INDEX

i-SPY

How to get your i-SPY certificate and badge

Let us know when you've become a super-spotter with 1000 points and we'll send you a special certificate and badge!

HERE'S WHAT TO DO!

✓ Ask an adult to check your score.

✓ Visit www.collins.co.uk/i-SPY to apply for your certificate. If you are under the age of 13 you will need a parent or guardian to do this.

✓ We'll send your certificate via email and you'll receive a brilliant badge through the post!